Key Stage 2

Our Bodies

Penny Johnson

Name _____

Schofield & Sims

Introduction

How does your body work? How can you keep healthy? In this book you will find out about food, diet and the different kinds of teeth that you have. You will learn about keeping healthy and different types of drugs and medicine. You will find out about human and animal skeletons, how muscles help you to move and about your heart and pulse rate. You will also learn about human life cycles and changes that happen to bodies over time.

How to use this book

Before you start using this book, write your name in the box on the first page.

Then decide how to begin. If you want a complete course to teach you all about bodies and how they work, you should work right through the book from beginning to end. Another way to use the book is to dip into it when you want to find out about a particular topic. The Contents page or the Index at the back of the book will help you to find the pages you need.

Whichever way you choose, don't try to do too much at once – it's better to work through the book in short bursts.

When you have found the topic you want to study, look out for the icons below, which mark different parts of the text.

Finally, use the Scientific investigation table on page 32 to find out how the **Understanding Science** series can help you use your new skills to investigate scientific questions in other topics.

Activities

These are the activities that you should complete. Write your answers in the spaces provided. After you have worked through all the activities on the page, turn to pages 33–37 at the end of the book to check your answers. When you are sure that you understand the topic, put a tick in the box beside it on the Contents page.

Explanation

This text explains the topic and gives examples. Read it before you start the activities. Any words shown like **this** appear in the combined Index and glossary. Turn to page 38 to see what these words mean.

Did you know?

Information

This text gives you useful background information and interesting facts about the subject.

Contents

What is in food?

Plants can make their own food. Animals (including humans) need to eat food because they cannot make their own.

Your body needs food:
- to give you energy to move around
- to help you grow
- to keep you **healthy**.

You need different kinds of food to help you do these things.

Food for energy

The things in food that give you energy are starch, sugar, fats and oils.

Starch is found in bread, pasta, rice and cereals.

Sugar is found in sweets, cakes, biscuits and fizzy drinks.

Fats and oils are found in milk, cheese, cooking oils, butter and meat.

Foods to help you grow

Meat, fish, milk, cheese, eggs, beans and lentils all help you grow.

Foods to keep you healthy

Fruit and vegetables help to keep you healthy.

1. Write down three things that your body needs food for.

_____

_____

_____

2. Tick the boxes to show what your body uses these foods for.
(You can have more than one tick for some foods.)

Food	For energy	For growth	For health
bread			
meat			
carrots			
eggs			
cheese			

3. There are different things in food that give you energy.
Tick the boxes to show which kind is in these foods.

Food	Starch	Sugar	Fats and oils
bread			
sweets			
cheese			
pasta			
meat			

Did you know? Food labels can tell you what is in the food. Proteins help you grow. Carbohydrates give you energy. Fibre helps your body to work properly.

Nutrition – Brown bread	
	Each slice contains
Energy	490 kJ
Protein	5.4g
Carbohydrate	20.2g
of which sugars	1.7g
Fat	1.5g
Fibre	2.5g

A balanced diet

You need to eat lots of different food to grow, stay **healthy** and get the energy you need. This is called **nutrition**. Your **diet** is all the different kinds of food you eat. You have a **balanced diet** when you have the right mixture of different food to give your body everything it needs.

You need some kinds of food for growth. You need a little more of the kinds for health and you need a lot more of the kinds that give you energy. These should be mainly the ones that contain starch, not those which have a lot of sugar or fats and oils.

1. Write down three different examples of food you need for each of the following:

a) health _____

b) growth _____

c) energy _____

(See pages 4 and 5 if you need some help.)

You can use a food triangle to remind you how much you need to eat of different kinds of food to achieve a balanced diet.

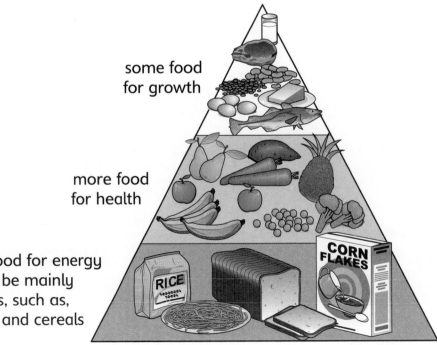

some food
for growth

more food
for health

even more food for energy
– this should be mainly
starchy foods, such as,
bread, pasta and cereals

A balanced diet

There are many different ways of getting a **balanced diet**. People in different countries eat different foods and some people have different **diets** for other reasons. For example, vegetarians do not eat meat or fish, but they can still eat a healthy, balanced diet.

Scientists have not always known what we need to eat to get a balanced diet. One discovery was made by a doctor called James Lind. He investigated a disease called scurvy that sailors used to get. Scurvy makes your gums bleed and your **teeth** fall out and eventually you can die.

Dr Lind had a **theory** that there was something missing from the sailors' diets. He did an experiment to find out if his idea was right. He found some sailors with scurvy and gave each of them different things to eat or drink. The sailors who ate fruit got better. Dr Lind wrote about this in a report, published in 1753. We now know that we need to eat fresh fruit to stay healthy.

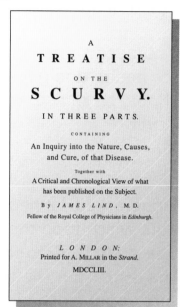

A
TREATISE
ON THE
SCURVY.
IN THREE PARTS.
CONTAINING
An Inquiry into the Nature, Causes, and Cure, of that Disease.
Together with
A Critical and Chronological View of what has been published on the Subject.
By *JAMES LIND*, M.D.
Fellow of the Royal College of Physicians in *Edinburgh.*

LONDON:
Printed for A. MILLAR in the *Strand.*
MDCCLIII.

2. What food can vegetarians eat to help them grow?

_____

3. Asha has some fish for her tea. What else should she eat to get everything her body needs from her meal?

_____

_____

4. a) What did James Lind think was the cause of scurvy? _____

_____

b) Was his idea right? _____

c) Explain your answer to part **b)**. _____

_____

Animal diets

Different animals need different foods in their **diet** to stay **healthy**. A pet rabbit only eats vegetables and leaves. A cat needs to eat meat or fish.

Anna and Luke are investigating pet diets.

I want to find out what kind of food cats like best.

Anna

I want to find out if dogs always eat meat.

Luke

Anna asked 12 people who owned cats which food their pets liked to eat. She drew a **pictogram** to show the **evidence** she collected. In her pictogram, each picture shows one cat.

Luke asked 10 different people what their dogs ate. He drew a **bar chart** to show his evidence.

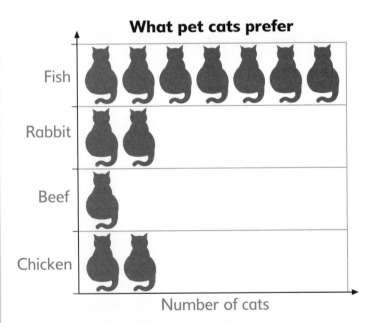

What pet cats prefer

Fish, Rabbit, Beef, Chicken

Number of cats

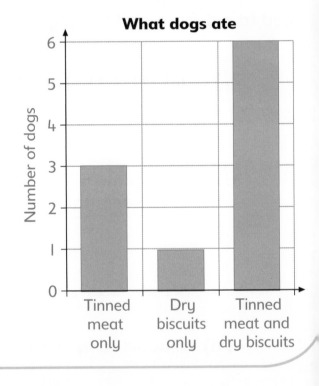

What dogs ate

Number of dogs

Tinned meat only | Dry biscuits only | Tinned meat and dry biscuits

1. a) Which was the favourite food for the cats? _____

b) How many cat owners said their cats preferred to eat rabbit? _____

2. a) How many dogs ate only tinned meat? _____

b) What did most of the dogs eat? _____

Animal diets

Anna and Luke are talking about their investigations. They are deciding how good their evidence is. This is an **evaluation**.

Anna

> Most cats like fish best.

> Oh! So my evidence might not be good enough to say that most cats like fish?

> Did all the owners let their cats try eating all the different kinds of food?

Luke

> There are thousands of cats in the country. You only asked 12 people.

3. a) Which of these is the best conclusion to Anna's investigation? Tick one box.

- [ ] Most cats like fish best.

- [ ] Most of the cats I asked about liked fish best.

b) Explain why you chose your answer to part **a)**.

_____

_____

4. Write a conclusion for Luke's investigation.

_____

_____

_____

You need to **digest** your food before your body can use it. This means breaking the food down so that it can be carried around your body in your blood. The parts of your body that do this are called the **digestive system**.

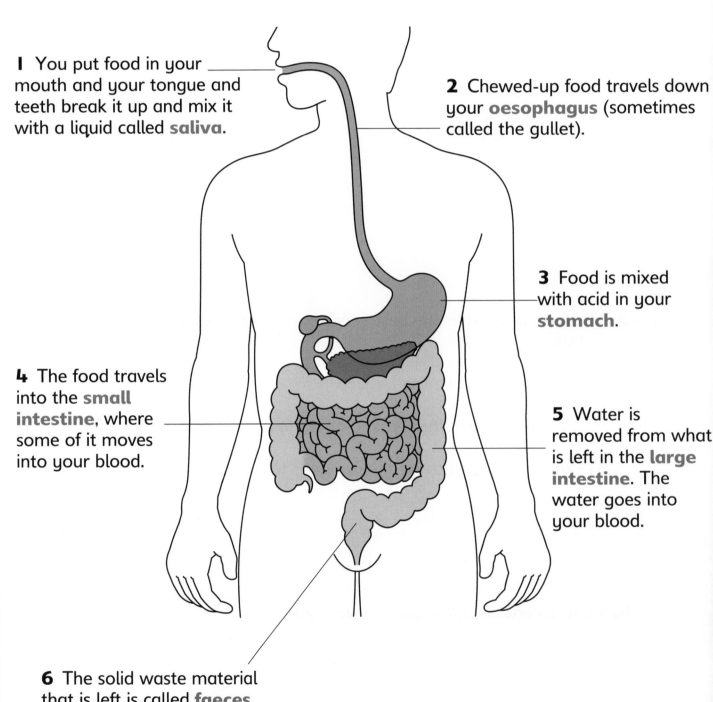

1 You put food in your mouth and your tongue and teeth break it up and mix it with a liquid called **saliva**.

2 Chewed-up food travels down your **oesophagus** (sometimes called the gullet).

3 Food is mixed with acid in your **stomach**.

4 The food travels into the **small intestine**, where some of it moves into your blood.

5 Water is removed from what is left in the **large intestine**. The water goes into your blood.

6 The solid waste material that is left is called **faeces**. This is stored in the **rectum** until you go to the toilet.

The digestive system

How to say some of the names
oesophagus – 'A-**soff**-a-gus'   stomach – '**stum**-ack'
faeces – '**fee**-sees'

1. Write down the parts of the digestive system that help to chop up your food into smaller pieces.

_____

2. Write down two parts of the digestive system where the food is mixed with a liquid.

_____

3. In which part does digested food move from the digestive system into your blood?

_____

4. Where is water taken from the food and moved into the blood?

_____

5. Some food cannot be digested.

a) What is this waste called? _____

b) Where is it stored? _____

c) How do you get rid of this waste?

_____

 **Did you know?** The time between eating some food and going to the toilet to get rid of the waste from that food is over 30 hours for children. It takes even longer for adults!

Teeth

When you were born you did not have any **teeth**. You started to grow your first set of teeth when you were about six months old. These first teeth are called your milk teeth and you have 20 of them.

When you are about six years old, a new set of teeth starts to grow and your milk teeth fall out to make space for them. These are your permanent teeth. You will eventually have about 32 of them.

1. a) What is your first set of teeth called? _____

b) What happens to these teeth? _____

2. What is your second set of teeth called? _____

You need teeth to help you eat. Your teeth have different shapes, because they do different jobs.

Incisors are at the front of your mouth. They are sharp, to help you cut up food into smaller pieces.

Canine teeth are next to the incisors. They are pointed, to tear food.

Molars are at the back of your mouth. They are used for chewing, crushing and grinding up food.

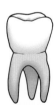

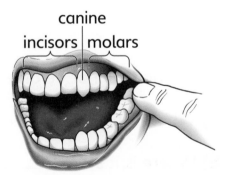

3. What are the three different kinds of teeth called?

_____

4. Which teeth do you use for chewing? _____

5. a) Label the incisors on the bottom part of the mouth diagram.

b) Label a canine tooth on the bottom part of the diagram.

Teeth

Animals have different-shaped **teeth**, to help them with the types of food they eat.

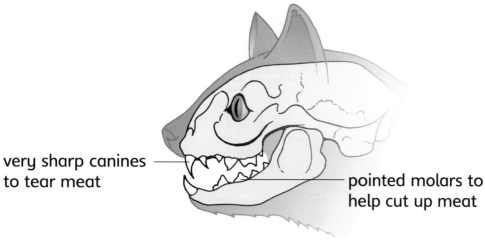

very sharp canines to tear meat

pointed molars to help cut up meat

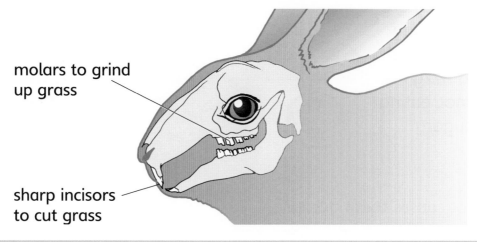

molars to grind up grass

sharp incisors to cut grass

6. a) What are the differences between human teeth and cat teeth?

_____

b) Why are human and cat teeth different?

_____

7. a) What are the differences between human teeth and rabbit teeth?

_____

_____

b) Why are human and rabbit teeth different?

_____

Micro-organisms are tiny living things that can only be seen if you use a microscope. Some micro-organisms can make your **teeth** decay. They feed on bits of food or sugar that are left in your mouth after you have eaten or drunk something. If a tooth starts to decay, a dentist will drill out the decayed part and fill the hole. If the tooth has decayed too much, the dentist will take it out.

You can look after your teeth by:
- brushing twice a day
- eating lots of foods such as carrots and apples and drinking milk (these foods are good for your body as well as your teeth)
- not drinking fizzy drinks and not eating sweets or sugary foods.

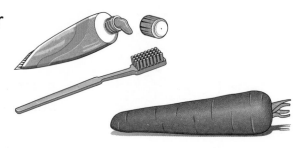

1. What causes tooth decay?

_____

_____

_____

2. Which foods are bad for your teeth? _____

3. How can you avoid tooth decay?

_____

_____

Keeping healthy

Your **lifestyle** (the things you do) can affect your health.
For a healthy lifestyle you need to:

- eat a **balanced diet**

- eat the right amount of food

- get enough sleep

- take some exercise several times a week

- keep your body clean and look after your teeth.

If you eat too much food, you will become fat. Being too fat is not healthy.
Being too thin is also unhealthy.

1. Sam walks to school and takes a packed lunch that includes an apple and an orange.

Jade's mum takes her to school in the car. Jade eats burgers and chips for lunch.

a) Who has the healthier lifestyle? _____

b) Give two reasons this person will be healthier.

_____

_____

2. Write down two reasons why watching television for six hours every day is not good for your health.

_____

_____

Drugs and medicines

A **drug** is a substance that changes the way your body works. A **medicine** is a drug that helps to make you feel better when you are ill.

Some medicines that make you better can also have other effects you do not want. For example, some kinds of cough mixture make you feel sleepy. Feeling sleepy is called a side effect of the medicine. You must never take medicine unless an adult has given it to you.

You can buy some medicines in the supermarket or a chemist's shop. These are medicines for things such as coughs and colds and sore throats. There is always a label on the packet or bottle telling you how much to take – you must never take more than the correct amount or it could make you ill.

Some medicines for more serious illnesses can only be given to you by a doctor. This is because they may be more dangerous if you take too much of them or they may have more serious side effects.

COUGH
MIXTURE

TAKE ONE
SPOONFUL THREE
TIMES A DAY

1. What are drugs? _____

2. Why is it important to read the instructions on a packet of medicine?

_____

_____

3. What is a side effect? _____

Did you know? Many plants contain substances that can be used as medicines. For example, people used to use the bark of willow trees to cure headaches and heart medicine used to be made from the leaves of foxglove plants.

However, substances made from plants can be dangerous, just as some drugs are dangerous. So you should never eat plant parts unless you know for sure that it is safe to do so.

Drugs and medicines

Many **drugs** are medicines, but some are not.

Alcohol is a drug found in beer, wine and some other drinks. People sometimes drink it because it makes them feel good. If someone drinks too much alcohol, they may feel very ill the next day. If they keep on drinking too much alcohol, it can permanently harm their body.

Tobacco contains drugs that people breathe in when they smoke cigarettes. However, the substances in cigarette smoke can damage the **heart** and lungs.

You can find out more about the dangers of drugs such as alcohol and tobacco by talking to an adult.

4. a) Write down the names of two drugs that are not medicines.

_____

b) Why is it a bad idea to drink too much alcohol?

_____

c) How can smoking tobacco harm you?

_____

If you feel your head, your chest or your hands, you can feel hard parts under your skin. These are your **bones**. The bones are part of your **skeleton**.

Your skeleton helps to protect parts of your body. Your skull protects your brain, and your ribs protect your **heart** and lungs.

Your spine helps to support your body.

Joints allow you to move.

Other animals also have bony skeletons inside their bodies. All animals that have a spine (backbone) are part of a group of animals called **vertebrates**.

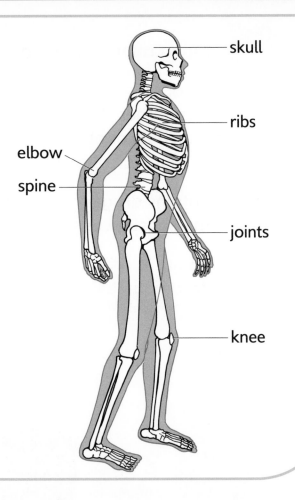

1. Write down three jobs that your skeleton does.

_____

_____

_____

2. a) Which part of your skeleton protects your lungs? _____

   b) Which part protects your brain? _____

3. Why do you need joints in your arms and legs?

_____

Did you know? There are 206 bones in your body. Over half of these bones are in your hands and feet.

Animals without skeletons

All animals need some support for their bodies, but not all animals have a bony **skeleton** inside their bodies. These animals are called **invertebrates**.

A woodlouse has a hard outer covering that protects it and supports its body.

A worm does not have any hard parts. Its body is supported by a watery liquid inside it.

1. a) Are the hard parts of a crab on the inside or the outside?

_____

hard covering

b) How do these hard parts help the crab?

_____

_____

2. Name one other animal that has hard parts on the outside.

_____

3. A slug does not have any hard parts. How do you think its body is supported?

_____

You can move around because you have **joints** in your **skeleton**. **Muscles** attached to the **bones** near your joints can make the bones move.

Your muscles work by contracting (getting shorter). When a muscle contracts it pulls on your bones.

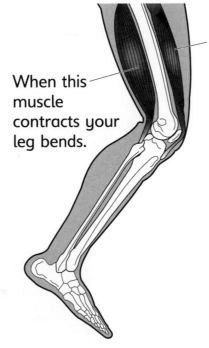

When this muscle contracts your leg bends.

When this muscle contracts your leg straightens.

Your muscles can only pull. They cannot push. This means that you need two muscles for each joint, one muscle to bend it and one to straighten it. When one muscle is contracting, the other one is relaxing (getting longer).

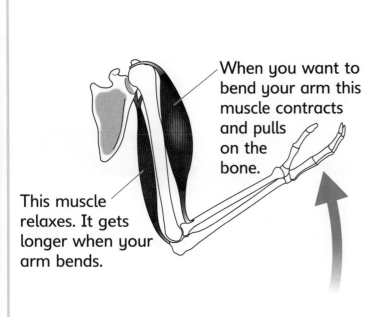

When you want to bend your arm this muscle contracts and pulls on the bone.

This muscle relaxes. It gets longer when your arm bends.

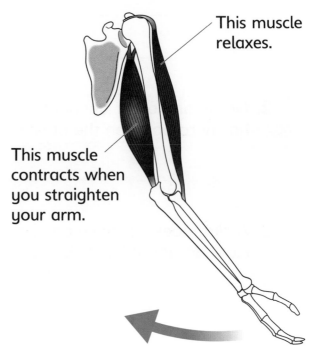

This muscle relaxes.

This muscle contracts when you straighten your arm.

1. What do muscles do?

_____

2. a) What does 'contract' mean?

_____

b) What happens to a muscle when it relaxes?

_____

3. Why do you need two muscles at each joint? _____

_____

_____

4. The diagram shows some of the muscles in your lower leg.

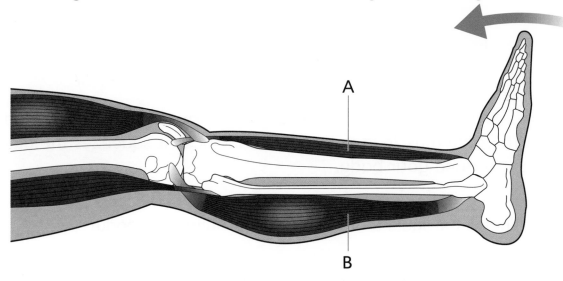

A

B

a) Which muscle needs to contract to move your foot in the direction of

the arrow? _____

b) What will happen to the other muscle?

_____

c) Imagine you are standing up. Which muscle would contract if you

wanted to stand on your toes? _____

Your **muscles** allow you to move your body. Muscles need energy to do this and they get the energy from the food that you eat. The food is carried to the muscles and all the other parts of your body in your **blood**. Your **heart** pumps blood around your body.

Your heart is in your chest. Your ribs help to protect your heart.

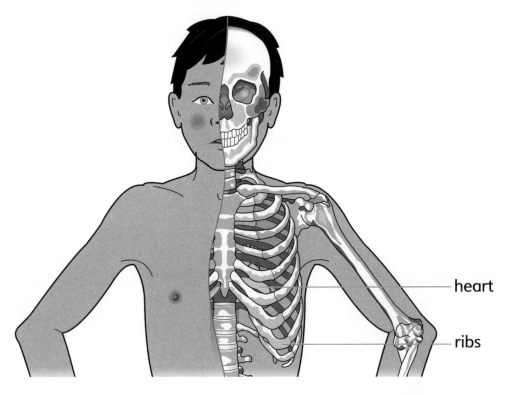

heart

ribs

Your heart is mainly made of muscle. It has hollow spaces inside it that are full of blood. When the muscle in your heart contracts, it squeezes the blood out and pumps it around your body.

1. What is the liquid that carries food around your body? _____

2. How is this liquid pumped around your body?

_____

3. a) What is your heart mainly made of? _____

b) How does it pump blood?

_____

_____

The **blood vessels** are tubes that carry **blood** around your body. The blood vessels that carry blood away from your **heart** are called arteries. The blood vessels that carry blood back to your heart to be pumped again are called veins.

Your heart and blood vessels make up your **circulatory system**.

Your blood carries **nutrients** (digested food) and water around your body.

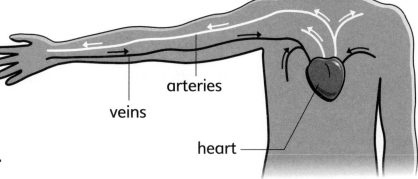

arteries

veins

heart

4. This diagram shows a heart. Label it using words from the box.

| artery | muscle | vein |

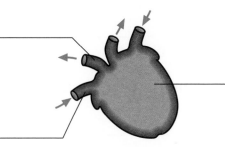

5. Match up the parts of your body with the jobs they do. One has been done for you.

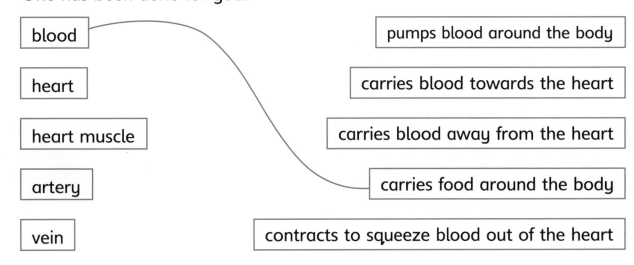

blood

heart

heart muscle

artery

vein

pumps blood around the body

carries blood towards the heart

carries blood away from the heart

carries food around the body

contracts to squeeze blood out of the heart

Did you know? William Harvey (1578–1657) was the first scientist to work out how the blood was pumped by the heart round the rest of the body.

Pulse rate and exercise

Activities such as running or playing games, such as football or rounders, give your body **exercise**. You need exercise to keep your **heart** and **muscles** strong.

When you run around, you start to feel hot. You may breathe faster and you can sometimes feel your heart beating faster. This happens because your muscles are working hard and need more food carried to them in your **blood**.

1. Write down three different kinds of exercise that you do.

_____

2. Describe how you feel when you have been exercising.

_____

_____

3. Why do you need to exercise?

_____

_____

When your heart beats, it pushes blood through your **blood vessels**. You can feel the blood being pushed if you gently feel your wrist or your neck. The movement you feel is called your **pulse**. Each beat of the pulse you can feel is one beat of your heart.

Your pulse rate gets faster when you exercise and it takes a little while for it to go down again when you stop exercising.

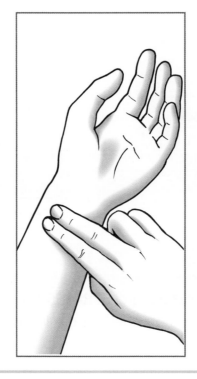
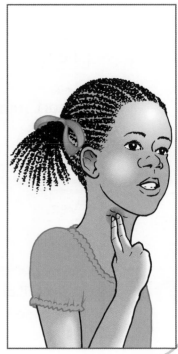

4. Why does your pulse rate go up when you exercise?

_____

_____

Jamelia's pulse rate

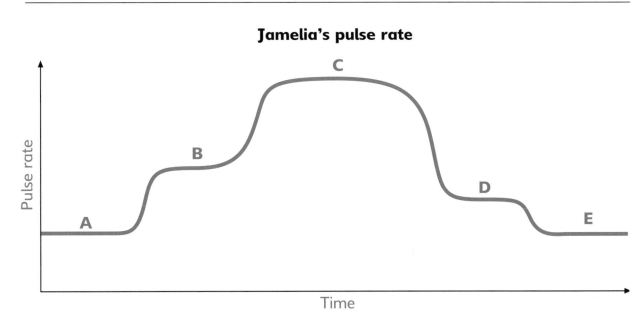

5. a) The graph shows Jamelia's pulse rate when she went home from school. Match up the letters on the graph with what Jamelia was doing. The first one has been done for you.

Jamelia is sitting in the classroom.	A
Jamelia runs around in the park with her friends.	☐
Jamelia sits down to watch TV.	☐
Jamelia walks home slowly.	☐
Jamelia walks to the park with her friends.	☐

b) Explain how you worked out your answers to part **a)**.

_____

_____

Did you know? Your **muscles** need oxygen as well as food to make them work. **Blood** carries oxygen from your lungs to your muscles. Your muscles produce carbon dioxide when they work and the blood carries this to your lungs so you can breathe it out.

Resting pulse rates

Your **heart** beats at its slowest rate when you are sitting still. This is called your resting **pulse** rate. You measure your pulse rate by counting the number of beats you can feel in one minute.

Vati measured her resting pulse rate five times.

Pulse rate (beats per minute)	83	86	95	80	84

1. a) Vati thinks she might have been moving around when she took one of the measurements. Which one do you think it was?

_____

b) Explain why moving around would have changed her resting pulse rate.

_____

_____

_____

2. Vati wrote down her resting pulse rate as 83 beats per minute. Why do you think she chose this number?

_____

_____

_____

Did you know? Some kinds of **medicine** make your heart beat faster. If you use an inhaler for asthma, you may find that you have a higher pulse rate than your friends. Your resting pulse rate gets lower as you get older. It is around 130 beats per minute when you are one year old and will be somewhere between 50 and 90 beats per minute when you are an adult.

Twenty pupils in Class 6 measured their **pulse** rates.
These are their results.

| 78 | 103 | 70 | 80 | 81 | 98 | 84 | 75 | 85 | 94 |
| 105 | 82 | 88 | 78 | 79 | 81 | 91 | 86 | 96 | 89 |

You could draw a **bar chart** using these numbers, but it would have a lot of bars! Instead, we put the numbers into groups.

Pulse rate range (beats per minute)	Tally	Total number of pupils
70–79	⊮	5
80–89	⊮ IIII	9
90–99		
100–109		

3. Complete the tally chart by counting the number of pupils with pulse rates between 90 and 99 beats per minute, and between 100 and 109 beats per minute. Now we can draw a bar chart to show the pulse rates in Class 6.

Pulse rates in Class 6

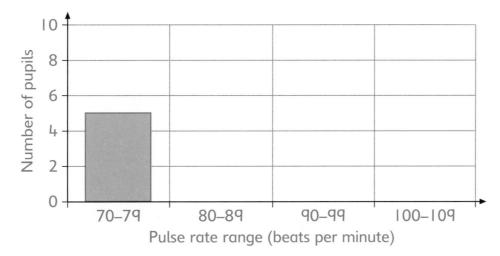

4. Finish drawing the bar chart, using the numbers from your tally chart.

5. a) What was the most common pulse rate range? _____

b) How many pupils had pulse rates in this range? _____

c) How many pupils had pulse rates in the lowest range? _____

Investigating pulse rates

When you **exercise** your **pulse** rate goes up. When you stop exercising it takes a few minutes for your pulse rate to go back to normal.

Rani and Liam are going to investigate pulse rates. They make predictions about what they think they will find out.

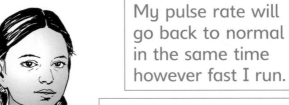

My pulse rate will go back to normal in the same time however fast I run.

Liam

If I run faster, my pulse rate will get higher.

Rani

Rani ran up and down the playground slowly for two minutes. She rested for five minutes, then ran faster for two minutes. The **line graph** shows her pulse rates.

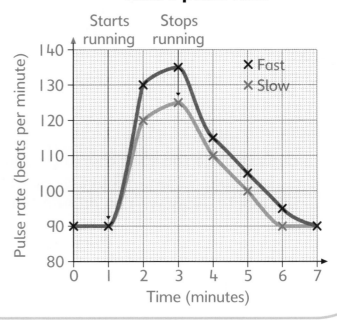

Rani's pulse rate

(Graph: x-axis "Time (minutes)" 0 to 7; y-axis "Pulse rate (beats per minute)" 80 to 140. Labels "Starts running" and "Stops running". Legend: ✕ Fast, ✕ Slow.)

1. a) When was Rani's pulse rate highest? Tick one box.

☐ When she was running slowly.

☐ When she was running fast.

b) What was her highest pulse rate? _____

2. How long did it take Rani's pulse rate to get back to normal after she

stopped running slowly? _____

3. Was Rani's prediction right? _____

Liam did the same as Rani. The table shows his results.

Liam drew a line graph to show his results.

| Time (mins) | Pulse rate (beats per min) | |
	Slow run	Fast run
0	75	75
1	75	75
2	110	120
3	115	130
4	100	110
5	85	95
6	75	80
7	75	75

Liam's pulse rate

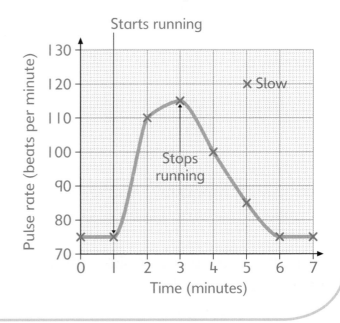

4. Finish drawing the graph.

5. a) Did Liam's pulse rate return to normal in the same time after both runs?

_____

b) Was his prediction correct?

_____

6. The two graphs (above and on page 28) show that the pulse rate went up more when the children ran faster. Liam says this means that Rani's prediction was right. Why is it wise to test more than one person to see if a prediction is correct?

_____

_____

Human life cycles

Animals are very small when they are born and change as they get older. The changes that happen to an animal are called its **life cycle**. The diagram below shows the human life cycle.

You were growing inside your mother for nine months before you were born.

Baby
Your parents look after you and do everything for you.

Child
You can do some things for yourself, but you still need your parents to help you.

Adult
When you are 18 you can look after yourself completely. You are old enough to have a baby of your own.

Adolescent
Your body begins to change when you are about 12 years old.

Humans need to be looked after for a long time after they are born. Humans often need to be looked after when they are very old, too. Old people are often unwell and may have weak bones and muscles.

1. Write down two ways in which your parents look after you.

_____

_____

2. What can you do for yourself that you could not do when you were a baby

_____

_____

3. What will you be able to do when you are an adult that you cannot do now?

_____

_____

Puberty is the time in your life when you are changing from a child to an adult. These changes happen while you are an adolescent.

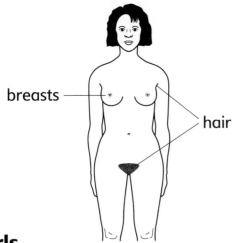

breasts — hair

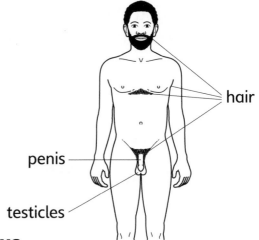

hair

penis —

testicles —

Girls
- Breasts develop.
- Hips get wider.
- Hair starts to grow on the body.
- Bodies change inside so they are ready to start having babies.

Boys
- Voice gets lower.
- Hair starts to grow on the body and face.
- Penis and testicles get larger.
- Bodies change so they are ready to start making babies.

1. Write down two changes that happen to both boys and girls during puberty.

_____

_____

_____

2. Write down two changes that only happen to girls.

_____

_____

3. Write down two changes that only happen to boys.

_____

_____

Scientific investigation

In this book you have found out about human and animal bodies, how they work and how they change. You have also learnt how to ask scientific questions. Good scientists need many different skills in order to investigate things. You can learn some of the other skills you need in the other **Understanding Science** books. The table below shows you the skills you need and which books help to teach you these skills or give you practice in using them.

Skill	Book pages					
	Animals & Plants	Our Bodies	Using Materials	Changing Materials	Forces & Electricity	Light, Sound & Space
Planning an investigation						
Asking a scientific question			10		6	
Knowing what variables are	6–7			8, 22, 24		8–9, 14
Planning a fair test	6–7		10–11, 20–21	8–9	6–7, 12	8–9, 14
Predicting what you think you will find out		28–29			6–7	14
Recording and presenting your evidence						
Making tally charts		27				
Drawing pictograms		8				
Drawing bar charts		8, 27	12–13, 20	22–23, 24–25		
Drawing line graphs		28–29		10, 22–23, 24–25	17, 19	8–9
Considering your evidence and evaluating it						
Writing a conclusion	6–7	9	12–13, 20	9, 10, 25	7, 13, 17–19	
Evaluating your investigation	6–7	9, 26	13	9, 10	13, 17	15

Answers

1. Energy, growing, keeping healthy.

2.

Food	For energy	For growth	For health
bread	✓		
meat	✓	✓	
carrots			✓
eggs		✓	
cheese	✓	✓	

3.

Food	Starch	Sugar	Fats and oils
bread	✓		
sweets		✓	
cheese			✓
pasta	✓		
meat			✓

Pages 6 and 7

1. a) You should have written down the names of any three fruits or vegetables.
b) Any three from: meat, fish, milk, cheese, eggs, beans, lentils.
c) Any three from: bread, pasta, rice, cereals. (You could have written down sweets, cakes, biscuits, fizzy drinks, milk, cheese, cooking oils, butter or meat, but it is better to eat starchy foods to get energy.)

2. Milk, cheese, eggs, beans or lentils.

3. Some fruit or vegetables and some energy food, such as bread, rice or pasta.

4. a) Something missing from the sailors' diet.
b) Yes.
c) He did an experiment and found that eating fresh fruit would stop the sailors getting scurvy.

Pages 8 and 9

1. a) Fish.
b) 2

2. a) 3
b) Tinned meat and dry biscuits.

3. a) Most of the cats I asked about liked fish best.
b) You should have written something like: there are a lot of cats and if you asked more people you might get a different answer.

4. Most of the dog owners I asked said their dogs ate tinned meat and dry biscuits.

Page 11

1. Teeth, tongue.

2. Mouth, stomach.

3. Small intestine.

4. Large intestine.

5. a) Faeces.
  b) Rectum.
  c) Go to the toilet.

Pages 12 and 13

1. a) Milk teeth.
  b) They fall out when permanent teeth start to grow.

2. Permanent teeth.

3. Incisors, canines and molars.

4. Molars.

5.

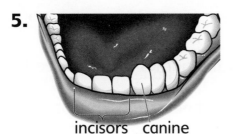

incisors   canine

6. a) Cats have bigger and sharper canines and pointed molars.
  b) Cats eat more meat **or** we eat different things.

7. a) Rabbits have bigger incisors and no canine teeth.
  b) Rabbits eat lots of grass.

Page 14

1. Micro-organisms feeding on food or sugar left in our mouths.

2. Sweet and sugary foods.

3. Brush your teeth and avoid eating sweets or foods with sugar in them.

Page 15

1. a) Sam.
  b) He has a healthier diet and gets more exercise.

2. You are not getting any exercise while you are watching television. You may not get enough sleep if you stay up and watch television.

Answers

Pages 16 and 17

1. Substances that change the way your body works.

2. Taking too much medicine can make you ill.

3. An effect of a medicine that you do not want.

4. a) Alcohol and tobacco.
   b) It could make you ill the next day or harm your body.
   c) It damages the heart and lungs.

Page 18

1. Protects parts of the body, supports the body and the joints let you move.

2 a) Ribs.
   b) Skull.

3. So they can bend or so you can move.

Page 19

1. a) Outside.
   b) They protect it, support it and let it move.

2. Woodlouse. (There are other animals you could have written down, such as lobsters, spiders, ants and so on.)

3. By a watery liquid inside it.

Page 21

1. Let you move your body by moving the bones.

2. a) Get shorter.
   b) It gets longer.

3. Muscles can only pull, not push, so each joint needs at least one muscle to bend it and another muscle to straighten it.

4. a) A
   b) It will relax and get longer.
   c) B

Pages 22 and 23

1. Blood.

2. By your heart.

3. a) Muscle.
   b) The muscle contracts and squeezes blood out.

4.

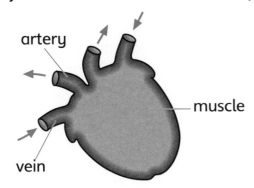

artery

muscle

vein

Answers

5. Heart – pumps blood around the body.
Heart muscle – contracts to squeeze blood out of the heart.
Artery – carries blood away from the heart.
Vein – carries blood towards the heart.

Pages 24 and 25

1. You should have written down three things such as running, jumping, playing football and so on.

2. Hot, tired, sweaty, breathing harder.

3. To keep your heart and muscles strong.

4. The muscles are working hard, so they need more food taken to them by the blood.

5. a) Jamelia runs around in the park with her friends – C.
Jamelia sits down to watch TV – E.
Jamelia walks home slowly – D.
Jamelia walks to the park with her friends – B.
b) The faster she is moving, the higher her pulse rate.

Pages 26 and 27

1. a) 95 beats per minute.
b) Her muscles work harder when she is moving, so her pulse rate is higher.

2. It is in the middle of all the numbers except the one when she was moving.

3. 4 people are in the 90–99 range.
2 people are in the 100–109 range.

4.

Pulse rates in Class 6

5. a) 80–89 beats per minute.
b) 9
c) 5

Pages 28 and 29

1. a) When she was running fast.
 b) 135 beats per minute.

2. 3 minutes.

3. Yes.

4.

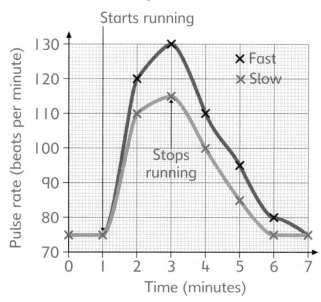

Liam's pulse rate

5. a) No.
 b) No.

6. People's pulse rates might be affected differently when they exercise.

Page 30

1. Any two from: provide a home, provide clothes, provide food, take me to school, play with me, buy me toys.

2. You could have written down some of these things: eat, drink, walk, get dressed, wash, go to the toilet.

3. You could have written down some of these things: drive a car, get a job, have babies.

Page 31

1. Hair starts to grow on the body, bodies change to become ready to start making babies.

2. Breasts develop, hips get wider.

3. Voice gets lower, penis and testicles get larger, hair starts to grow on the face.

Index and glossary

Index and glossary